GREAT EXPECTATIONS

GREAT EXPECTATIONS

Charles Dickens

An imprint of Om Books International

First published in 2013 by

An imprint of Om Books International

Corporate & Editorial Office
A-12, Sector 64, Noida 201 301
Uttar Pradesh, India
Phone: +91 120 477 4100
Email: editorial@ombooks.com
Website: www.ombooksinternational.com

Sales Office
4379/4B, Prakash House, Ansari Road
Darya Ganj, New Delhi 110 002, India
Phone: +91 11 2326 3363, 2326 5303
Fax: +91 11 2327 8091
Email: sales@ombooks.com
Website: www.ombooks.com

ISBN: 978-93-83202-60-7

Printed in India

10 9 8 7 6 5 4 3 2 1

Contents

1. A Strange Place to Meet

I have lived in Kent for most of my life, but even today, the marshes can still frighten me. The gathering mist would throw figures all around and strange sounds would always come out of the hazy atmosphere. It was the same that evening; on Christmas Eve, when I had gone to visit the graves of my parents in the churchyard on the marshes. My parents had died when I was very young. So all I knew about them was what I could read from their tombstones. I was named after my father, Philip Pirrup. Since I could never pronounce it properly, I shortened it to 'Pip', myself. That particular evening, I felt very lonely, as if I was all alone in the world. Lost in the cofounded mist, I started to cry.

A minute later, a hoarse voice rang through the churchyard, "Stop that or I'll tear you to pieces!"

A large man came out of nowhere. He had an evil expression on his face. He was wearing mud-stained grey clothes. He also had an iron clamp around one of his legs. Though his whole appearance was shabby, his eyes still glared brightly at me.

I was so scared at meeting this horrendous looking man in the graveyard that I could barely move. I just managed to mumble, "Please spare me, please spare me ..."

He did not pay any heed to what I said, and grabbing me by my hair, said, "Quick, what's your name and where are you from, kid? Where do you stay?"

Even before I could think about what to say, the words started coming out of me automatically. "The name's Pip, Sir! My parents are down in those graves and I live with my sister, Mrs. Joe Gargery and her husband, the village blacksmith."

The information seemed to have pleased the man, as he released me. "You live with the blacksmith, eh?" he asked.

Without waiting for an answer, he suddenly went through my pockets and discovered the small loaf of bread I carried. He pushed me on to a tombstone and started tearing into that little loaf. Once he was through, he turned to me and asked, "Tell me something boy ... You know what a file is?"

I knew what he was talking about and therefore, I nodded my head.

"Well, it's like this ... You come back tomorrow in the morning with a file and also some food to eat. I think then I shall let you live, you understand me?" he enquired.

I just shook my head somehow. He must have thought that I had replied in the affirmative, so he let me go. I started to run as fast as I could to get as far as I could from this strange evil man.

However, another kind of fear awaited me at home! As soon as I managed to get in through the kitchen door, my brother-in-law, Joe, simply stared at me and I knew what the problem was. My sister had been looking for me. Joe came to me and asked, "Where have you been, Pip?"

Even before I could answer, the front door slammed shut and soon, my sister was standing there in front of me. She was nearly twenty years older than me and was well known throughout the village for her bad temper. The minute she laid her eyes on me, she came charging in, as if she wanted to tear me into two.

Just as she was about to get a hold of me, Joe stepped in between us. My sister tried to get round him, but Joe was a giant. She even tried to swing around and get me, but Joe and I kept changing our directions, making it almost impossible for her to reach me. Completely exhausted, she eventually gave up trying to reach me.

Joe and I exchanged sly smiles. However, my smile vanished just as a huge cannon fire sounded outside. My heart almost skipped a beat, but Joe calmed me down and told me, "It's from the

prison. They fire cannons to inform the people about convicts escaping. And that's the second one. We heard one yesterday, too ..." A cold shiver ran down my spine.

My sister shouted at us, harshly, to come to the table for dinner. While she was buttering Joe's slice of bread, I quietly slipped my own loaf into my pocket. Now I would at least have something to give to my convict, later.

I soon slipped away into my room, terrified about what would happen in the morning. It was not a pleasant night. Since, for as long as I could sleep, I dreamt about horrible occurrences, such as ending up in prison because of stealing food from my sister's pantry. Eventually, a flash of lighting woke me up pretty early. I could see that it was still dark outside.

I quickly yet quietly slipped into the pantry, careful not to disturb anyone. As Christmas was around the corner, there was a lot of food in the house. I took some more bread, some cheese, and

also a pork pie, which had been kept at the back of the pantry. I guessed that my sister would not need all these things immediately. I also poured some wine into a bottle.

I then slid away into Joe's workshop and chose a thick, heavy file for the convict. Quite soon, I was off towards the marshes to meet my runaway convict.

2. Another!

Being in the marshes at this time of the day was spookier than ever. It was so dark that I could not see a thing. I groped around, relying completely on my sense of direction. As the mist cleared a little bit, I could see the convict sitting at a distance, near the tombstones. It seemed to me that he had fallen asleep, his head buried deep in his chest.

As I went and placed my hand on his shoulder, he jumped up and raised his hand to hit me. Oh! But this was not the man I was supposed to meet! This was someone else. Perhaps, he was the man who had escaped from prison last night.

As the second convict bent forward to grab me, I jumped out of the way, making him stumble and fall. I realised that he was quite weak; hence, he must have been cold and ill. However, before he could get up and take another shot at me, I ran off into the darkness, far away from him.

It was only then that I came across the convict who had caught me yesterday. He was walking around in circles, presumably trying to warm himself and keep himself awake. As I crept closer to him, he suddenly saw me and came running towards me. He spotted the file in my hand, for it was so big that I could not put it into my pocket. He, at once, grabbed it from me and started to work on the chain that was tied to his feet.

While the convict worked on the chain, I offered him the food that I had brought for him. He grabbed the piece of bread, ravenously. Then, he saw the bottle in my hand and gestured towards it. "Wine, Sir!" I said and he at once snatched the bottle away from me. He murmured something that sounded like, "Well done, kid!"

The convict had been able to file off his chains and was now busy eating. I kept looking

incredulously at him. At one point, I asked him, "Aren't you going to save something for your friend?" At this, he stopped in the middle of his bite. It took him a good few moments before he turned to me. Again he mumbled something, but I kept quiet because I could not understand what he was telling me. Then he came closer to me. He did not look as frightening as he had the day before. Swallowing his food completely, he said, "What friend?"

I merely replied, "The one down there. He was wearing the same kind of clothes like you. I thought …" I wasn't allowed to complete my sentence. Taking a last swig from the bottle, he ran off into the darkness. After a while, convinced that the convict had gone and would not return, I started back for home.

3. The Thieves are Caught

Things at home were no different from the madness outside! My sister would not let us stand in any corner of the room. She was running up and down, cleaning every nook and corner of the parlour. The dust covers came off all the furniture and the best tableware that we had was out on display. The parlour was used only on special occasions, and today was Christmas Eve. Joe and I understood that guests would start pouring in during the evening, so we both retired to his workshop, where we could be at peace.

Just as we entered the workshop, a thought suddenly struck me and my worst fears came true! The pork pie! Now I understood why it had been kept at the back of the pantry. It was meant for the Christmas party tonight! This thought kept troubling my mind through the rest of the day, right till the point I was ready for the party, suffocating in my stiff clothes.

Slowly the guests started coming in. Many people came from the town, including Uncle Pumblechook. Though he was actually Joe's uncle, my sister had developed a special fondness for him, because he was rather rich in our circle of friends and family. She fussed over him, serving him before the others and always making sure that he was having fun. We, however, were given no such treatment!

After the meal, my heart started fluttering because I knew that my theft would soon be discovered. My sister, who had been in the pantry for a long time, came out and declared, "I can't understand it ... the pork pie that I had made ... it's gone!" I did not know what to do and kept looking at the table. The heated conversation at the table became louder and louder. I could not stand it any longer. I jumped off my chair and bolted towards the door.

The minute I opened the door to run away, I saw two guards standing just outside the door. Their handcuffs were dangling right before my eyes and everything seemed to go dark around me. I was sure that they had come to put me in prison. I was about to faint with fright, however, just then Joe came from behind and held me. His strong hands made me feel a little better.

One of the guards smiled at me and said, "I am sorry to intrude upon your festivities at this hour, but I come here in search of a blacksmith." My Sister, obviously annoyed at the rude interruption, pointed towards Joe. The man then turned to Joe and said, "My good man, I am a sergeant in the King's forces and we are about to capture a convict who had escaped sometime back. But you see, these handcuffs have to be repaired. Can you help us?"

Joe inspected the pair that was given to him and said, "It can be done, but it will take time." The sergeant merely smiled and said, "Oh, that's all right! We have till morning to catch the scoundrel. You can start and my men shall help you."

This break worked for my benefit, because in all this commotion everyone had forgotten about the pork pie. I breathed a sigh of relief as the sound of Joe's hammer clammered through the rest of the party. The sergeant joined us though and regaled us with stories of criminals. When Joe's work was finally done, the sergeant offered to take us along and witness the capturing of the convict. Joe agreed to go at once and asked my sister to let me go with him as well. Now I was once again lost in thought, for I felt that my convict might feel that I had betrayed him and had led the police on to his hideout.

However, it was a long time before the police could make any progress. Apparently, one of the guards had heard some shouts from a distance. When they travelled towards the place where the sound came from, they found two convicts fighting among themselves. One of them was the man whom I had brought food for and the

other was the man I had mistaken him for. The second convict was screaming in pain. The police separated them at once. While the other one was rather happy at being taken away by the police, claiming that he was about to be murdered, my convict kept yelling, "If I wanted, I could have killed him. But I would not let him escape. I could have run away, but I would not spare him."

The sergeant managed to capture both the men and pushed them towards the boat. As the convicts were being taken away, I tried to shake my head trying to tell my convict that it was not me who had led the police to him. I had not betrayed him.

Just as my convict was about to board the prison-boat, he turned to us and said, "I have a confession to make. While I was here in the marshes, I stole some food, a pork pie, and some wine from the blacksmith's house. Please forgive me for that."

Joe heard him and immediately replied, "That's alright! We wouldn't mind a hungry man

taking some of our food. Please don't think too much about it. Right, Pip?"

I was too scared to even talk, so I just shook my head nervously. Soon the boat disappeared into the mist. I breathed a sigh of relief.

4. An Unexpected Invitation

For us things returned to normal after that incident. Life went on as usual. Joe worked in his workshop and I would sit there all day long, learning what it was like to be a blacksmith. I always wanted to be like Joe. After all, he loved me and I loved him. Whenever my sister would try and hit me, Joe was the one who would always come and stand in between, thus, saving me from her anger. However, I did wonder how many times my sister beat Joe in my place!

One day, as I was with Joe in his workshop, Uncle Pumblechook came by. He had a rather interesting offer to make, and truth be told, we were all a little shaken by it. He said that Miss Havisham, an old lady who lived in an old, neglected house a little away from the town, had asked for me to come and play at her house.

When Joe heard this, his obvious question was, "How did the lady, who never leaves her house, hear about Pip?" It was true. No one had ever seen Miss Havisham, though she had always lived in the town. People had only heard about her. No one knew what she looked like, what she did, or anything about her. Therefore, it was quite strange that she had even heard about me.

My sister felt that this was a great opportunity for me. As far as she was concerned, she saw a rich woman wanting to take her brother under her wing. This could only mean that there would be an increase in her wealth. My sister added, "Your uncle is her tenant. One day, when he had gone to pay her the rent, she asked him if she knew of any such boy. Sweet Lord, he mentioned our Pip. Now, doesn't he have a heart of gold?"

Joe still looked quizzical, as if he wasn't completely convinced with the news. He

found the whole circumstance rather strange. However, my sister had already busied herself with cleaning me up, and so Joe realised that it would be best for him to keep quiet.

Goodness me, I had never smelt so clean in all my life! My sister took extra care to scrub me. She did not even spare the spots behind my ears. Soon I was dressed up in the best clothes that I had, and was all ready to go to this rich lady to entertain her.

As I was being prepared for my visit, my sister kept talking. "Oh I wish I were a boy, Pip. You are so fortunate!"

Even Uncle Pumblechook joined in with her. "Oh, I would say fortune is looking over our Pip. He is lucky, so lucky!"

A few minutes later, I was bundled off in Uncle Pumblechook's cart and we were on our way to meet this eccentric rich lady.

We stopped by an old house. It seemed that it had not been painted for the last twenty years; the greens in front of the house had turned into forests. I had a feeling that the whole thing was about to crumble and break over our heads. Uncle Pumblechook took me off the cart and we started to walk towards the main gate, which, too had turned to rust. As he rang the bell, a gentle voice came from somewhere and asked, "Who is it?" Uncle Pumblechook lowered his hat and said, "It is Pumblechook here with the boy, to see Miss Havisham." There was no response from the other end.

We kept waiting patiently for some more time, when suddenly we saw a young girl approach us from within. She was the most beautiful girl that I had ever seen in my whole life. There was elegance in her walk, in the way that she held her head, in the way she even looked at me. As she came closer, I realised that she was perhaps the same age as me.

She opened the door to let us in, but the minute Uncle Pumblechook tried to squeeze himself through, the girl almost trapped him within. Uncle Pumblechook gave her a scared but inquiring look,

and the girl merely asked, "Does Miss Havisham want to see you, too?" Uncle Pumblechook mumbled, "No ... I ... but if she ... maybe ..." "Oh, in that case she does not want to see you," said the girl, and shut the door on Uncle Pumblechook.

As we entered the house, I realised that I could see nothing. It was darker than a cave. The girl, who locked the door behind us, picked up a candle and there was just enough light to see where we were going. I kept following her for what felt like ages, and we kept going through turns and passageways. She kept reprimanding me throughout the way, "Don't stop, or you'll get lost. Walk faster."

Finally, we stopped in front of a large door. The girl pointed towards it and asked me to go in. I stepped back and said in my most courteous voice, "After you, Miss!"

She merely tossed her head, gave a short laugh and said, "I'm not going there." She left with the candle, leaving me momentarily in complete darkness.

I finally mustered enough courage to open the door and walk in. What I saw after that scared me even more, for I had never seen a room, or a person like that. It seemed to be a lady's dressing chamber, with a huge mirror in the middle of the room. There were clothes scattered all over and some half-full boxes lying around. As I looked through the room, I suddenly saw a lady sitting in the midst of this mess, dressed like a bride. She was wearing a bridal gown, all complete with satin, lace, and silk. A veil hung over her head. She, strangely, had one shoe on and the other was kept atop the dresser. Of course, I say white, but the fact was that with age, her bridal gown had turned yellow. The gown, being made for a young woman surely, now hung on this old woman, who had shrunk right to skin and bones.

As I stared at this lady, she suddenly gestured at me to come forward. With small, short steps I went closer to her till I was about an arm's length away from her. In a most eerie and squeaky voice she asked me harshly, "Who are you?"

"My name is Pip, Ma'am," I replied, shaking with fear. She put her hand forward and stroked my head. "Pip, Pip," she kept repeating it for a while and said, "What a lovely name ... Pip!" Then she took my hand in hers and placed it over her heart. I was dumbfounded and did not know what to do, or say. Miss Havisham then asked me, "Do you know what lies here, Pip?"

I did not even know if I was supposed to answer, or whether she would give me the answer herself. However, I saw that she was silent for a while, so I replied, "Your heart, Ma'am!" hoping that it would be the right answer. She just smiled at me and said, "Yes, and it's broken."

She then pointed towards the clock. I looked at it and saw that the time read twenty minutes to nine. Needless to say it had stopped working, just like everything else in that house seemed to have. She looked sadly at the clock, with my hand still in hers. Then she suddenly broke free of the trance that she was in and said, "I have been alone for a long time and now I want to be amused. So play!"

I had no idea what to do. What could I play with, standing there, alone? I started feeling very uncomfortable. When she saw me stand there and do nothing, she turned to me and said, "Call Estella, will you? If you can't play, you can at least do that, can't you?"

I immediately ran towards the door. I was happy to get away from her, even if it was for a short while. I stumbled back into the dark passageway and called out Estella's name for a while. Suddenly, I saw the flickering light of her candle come in from the right. Then, she entered the room without even looking at me.

Miss Havisham bid her to come closer and placed a brooch on her head. She then told her, "Some day, my child, this will be yours. And then you will be able to break the hearts of men. Now, play cards with this boy while I watch, will you?"

I did not understand what this meant, but I did not even want to know anything that went on in this madhouse. I was just waiting for Uncle

Pumblechook to come back and take me home. The minute Estella heard that she would have to play with me, she turned to Miss Havisham and said, "I won't play with him ... he is but a common peasant."

I then heard Miss Havisham whisper something in her ears, which made me want to run away from the house even sooner. "Maybe so, but you can still break his heart, can't you?"

We soon started playing. Estella kept laughing at me all the time, making fun of my clothes, my appearance and even how I called the knaves 'jacks'. I became so nervous at her remarks that I could not get my game right and, needless to say, I lost. That made Estella laugh at me some more.

Finally, as our game ended, Estella left as quietly as she had come in. Miss Havisham then drew me close and said, "Estella has being saying rather nasty things about you. You haven't said anything about her though ... Tell me, what do you think about her?"

I tried to stay quiet, hoping that she would go on to something else and forget about this question, but I was soon forced to answer. "She is very pretty, Ma'am ... but she is also very rude!"

Miss Havisham rested her head back, as if satisfied with the answer that I had given her. She then called Estella back and asked her to give me something to eat. Estella returned with a small portion of bread and meat. I felt like I was a dog who was being fed. I started to cry. Estella, on seeing this, gave me a small smile. Then, tossing her head, she was gone.

I felt a lot better at home that evening. Even my sister seemed to be more pleasant. However, Estella had changed me completely that day. It was only now that I realised that I was nothing more than a common peasant; that I had no place in this world. From that day on, I was not the same Pip any more.

5. For the First Time

I had to go back to Miss Havisham after another eight days. Once again, Estella led me to her room and disappeared into the flickering darkness without a word. Miss Havisham seemed to be more bearable this time, calling me towards her and saying, "You don't seem to play very well. Are you any good at work?"

I nodded, appreciating all the more the prospect of not having to see Estella again and be insulted by her. Miss Havisham then led me to another room. It seemed to be a ballroom, with a huge table in the centre. Spiders, mice, and cockroaches flitted about, as if they were dancing in celebration. I saw a huge silver stand at the centre of the table. It was covered in cobwebs;

however, what was strange was that an old, spoilt, smelly wedding cake stood upon it.

I just stood there, happily watching a few mice run around the cake. They were the only partakers of this feast and seemed to be enjoying it. I looked at the clock on the wall next to the table and saw that it also read twenty minutes to nine. This was the same time as the clock I had seen the first day. Just as I stood staring at it, Miss Havisham came from behind and asked me to lead her for a walk.

This is what I was required to do when I visited Miss Havisham's house. I would walk her around the house with her hand resting on my shoulders all the while. This was followed by a dog-like meal from Estella.

One day, I met with the first irregularity during my monotonous visits to Miss Havisham. Estella was leading me to Miss Havisham when a man started to walk down the steps. He was a burly-looking man, with large eyes and bushy eyebrows. As we passed each other, the man

asked Estella, "Who do we have here?" Estella merely quipped, "Oh, he's nobody Mr. Jaggers, just a boy!"

The man just looked on for a while and walked off.

The next day, another strange thing happened. Miss Havisham declared that she was rather tired that day and it would suffice that I just play with Estella. That day we played for a rather long time. Since I had more time, it became easier for me to adjust to Estella's tantrums. I actually started winning some games.

At the end of it, Miss Havisham was so pleased with me that she called me to her and spoke rather nicely to me. Estella kept looking at us from a distance, as if waiting to take me to the door to lead me out. As we walked away, Estella suddenly turned to me at the door and asked, "Would you like to kiss me?"

I was, of course, attracted to her right from the very beginning. When she asked me, I turned to her and kissed her on her cheek. Only then did

I realise the reason behind the kiss. She was just trying to chide me for playing well and winning a few games. She was just trying to insult me once again.

I never did value that kiss. It was an insult and a bad one.

These visits went on for around eight months or so. One day, Miss Havisham called me and asked me what I wanted to do with my life. I told her about my dreams to be Joe's apprentice and she encouraged me. She said that it was time to get the papers done.

So a few days later, Joe, my sister and Uncle Pumblechook took me to the Town Council and I was officially apprenticed to Joe. Joe was obviously very happy, as it was his dream to have me work with him. I was happy, but it was not the same thing for me any more. My visits to Miss Havisham and my interaction with Estella had changed my attitude completely.

I went to Miss Havisham with these papers and showed them to her. She smiled happily,

looking at the papers and gave me twenty crowns as a gift.

Then she said, "I am happy for you, Pip. However, let me remind you that you are not to come here any more. You now belong to Joe Gargery. Never come here, and never expect to get anything from here. Your relationship with this house is now over."

I never could understand these last words of Miss Havisham, even a long time after I last met her.

6. High Hopes

Life was never the same for me after that. I was now an apprentice to Joe, a dream that had been accomplished. Strangely, I was not happy. This was not the life that I wanted to lead any longer. All day long, as I would steam and sweat in the forge, watching Joe hammer away, I would always have the strange fear that Estella would one day peep through the forge window and laugh at my black hands and face.

Finally, I could not stand it any longer. I had to get out of the forge. Joe obviously did not mind my taking a day off. I went to see Miss Havisham again. However, a lady, who introduced herself to me as Miss Havisham's cousin, opened the gate this time. It looked as if she wanted to throw me out of the house at that very moment, but she dared not cross Miss Havisham, and so I was allowed to go in.

"I hope you have not come here for anything, because you surely will get nothing," Miss Havisham remarked, the minute her eyes fell on me. I merely said in reply, "No ma'am, I am not looking for anything. I just came to see you."

"Well in that case, it's alright! You can come and see me from time to time. Come on your birthday," she said. As she noticed me looking around the room casually, she said, "Looking for her, aren't you?"

I tried to hide my embarrassment as I said, "I was just wondering if she has been well ..."

Even before I could continue, prompt came the reply that dismissed my concerns with a nonchalant air. She said, "Oh! She has been better than ever. She's gone to Europe, learning to be a lady. She is now prettier than she ever was. Ha, ha, take a look at yourself! You think that you have lost her!" And the room was filled with her

hideous laughter. She did not even notice that I had left the room soon after.

The way back home was rather lonely. I kept wondering about the various things that had happened to me in the past. As I neared home I saw a small crowd gathered in front of the door. As I walked faster, the crowd parted to make room for me. Even before I could get in, Joe grabbed me from behind and said, "Relax, Pip! We have to be pretty brave about whatever happened. Someone came in and attacked your sister. The doctor is taking a look at her right now."

It was only then that I could see my sister. She lay sprawled on the kitchen floor, blood oozing from the back of her head. "Is she alive?" I exclaimed, worried to my very core. Without even looking up the doctor replied, "Yes, she is alive ... But I don't think she will ever be the same any more. The cut is pretty nasty."

Ever since that day, a huge change came over the house. My sister was no longer the way she used to be earlier. Now, she just sat in the corner

in front of the fireplace. She never could talk again and it seemed that she had lost her memory as well. Joe did feel a little strange at first, but later got used to the peace and quiet that he had never had till before the incident.

The pastor sent over his niece, Biddy, to take care of us. She was an amazing woman, who took real good care of the whole house. She was also one of the best cooks I had ever known. Under her care, I learned to read and write much faster, too.

Eventually, I confided to Biddy that I wanted to be a gentleman, come into a lot of money and live lavishly. Biddy never looked up from her sewing once, as she asked me, "All this, just for her?"

I was embarrassed; however, I did not deny it, as that was the truth!

7. Dreams

Many years passed and I forgot all about Miss Havisham and Estella. I kept working with Joe, learning all that a blacksmith should know. One day, as Joe and I were busy working away in the forge, we heard someone knock on the front door. As I went and opened the door, I saw Mr. Jaggers standing there. He was the same man who had met me on the steps of Miss Havisham's house. I could not mistake that face and those eyes. When Joe saw Mr. Jaggers standing at the door, he came rushing out of his workshop. Then, he immediately started taking the dust covers off the furniture, inviting Mr. Jaggers to come in and sit.

As Mr. Jaggers sat down on the chair by the table, he looked calm and composed, as if he had a lot to say. He first placed his hat on the table and took a good look at the two of us. He started by addressing Joe. "Mr. Gargery, I come here regarding your apprentice, this young boy, Pip. What I am about to say will be about his future, and a great one at that! I hope you will not stand in his way, will you?"

Joe, who seemed to be as surprised as I was with Jaggers' proposal, shook his head and said, "I wouldn't dream of it, Sir ... please continue!"

Acknowledging Joe's reply, Jaggers then began telling us his true reason for coming to Kent. He said, "I am a lawyer, a rather successful lawyer in London and I have come here to talk to Pip about his future at the behest of one of my clients." Mr. Jaggers' speech shocked me. He continued, "It is the wish of my client that Pip be relieved as your apprentice and come over to London, where he will start to lead the life of a gentleman. Needless to say, he will come into a lot of money and property. My client will take care of every need that Pip may have. For starters, my client

has asked me to enquire, Mr. Gargery, whether you would like to take some money to relieve Pip from your own services?"

Joe, who was still unable to understand what was happening, could only say, "Like I said Mr. Jaggers, I will not stand in the way of Pip's grand future. I have loved him since he was a small child and he means everything to me. I just want him to lead a good and happy life, nothing more."

Jaggers considered the reply and said, "Well then, I shall now tell you about the rest. As I mentioned, everything will be taken care of. Pip's lodgings, his food, clothes, education, absolutely everything! I will of course be controlling the money that he gets; so Pip, you can consider me your guardian in London."

I could hardly believe what was being said in the room. It was as if my dreams were about to come true. I had never thought that this was possible. I had never thought that this could actually happen. But, Jaggers was not done yet …

"However, there are a couple of issues that I need to talk about, which are of utmost importance during this deal. Your benefactor desires that you should always have the name Pip. And secondly, your benefactor also wants to remain anonymous. If ever you get to know his or her name, you are not to disclose it to anyone, not even to me. Is that understood?"

I knew who my benefactor was. It had to be Miss Havisham. She had finally decided to take care of me and make me a gentleman worthy of Estella. I nodded to show my agreement to the two conditions that Jaggers had kept before me.

Now that he was finished, Jaggers got up and laid some money on the table, a sum of about twenty-five guineas. He then turned to me and said, "This money is for your travel to London. Also please get some new clothes made for your journey. Once you are in London, you will reside with a certain gentleman, called Herbert Pocket. His father will be your tutor. Do I make myself clear?"

Joe and I could not respond. We did not know what to say. Long after Jaggers had left, we just kept sitting there, looking into the empty space before us. Biddy came by a little later and saw us in that state. She enquired as to what had happened. It was only then that Joe came to his senses and told her all that had just transpired. He then rushed off to explain matters to my sister, who needless to say, did not understand a word.

Now that Biddy and I were alone, she turned to me and said, "So Pip, at least one of your dreams is about to come true!"

Yes, one of my dreams was about to come true! And I had Miss Havisham to thank for that.

8. The Big City

The next day, I started to make preparations to leave for London. I immediately went to Mr. Trabb's shop. He was the local tailor in the village. His attendant told me to wait because Mr. Trabb was still eating his breakfast. After a while, since it was taking him a surprising amount of time to finish eating, I mentioned to his attendant in a loud voice, "Please tell Mr. Trabb that I have come into a lot of money and need a new suit to travel to London. But since he is busy, I'll come back some other time."

No sooner had I finished, Mr. Trabb came rushing into the room, a large smile glazing his fat face. Within a few moments, there was a flurry of activity in the shop. Several bales of cloth were unrolled and quick measurements were taken. Trabb even went on to give me a compliment, saying that my body would make any suit look good. The power of money could buy almost anything!

A few days later, when I was about to go away to London, I decided to call on Miss Havisham one last time. She was happy to see me and declared that she had learnt of my good fortune from Mr. Jaggers. As I was about to leave, she said, "Remember, you shall always have the name Pip." I wanted to thank her, but I remembered Jaggers' conditions. I could not reveal her name or even pretend that I knew who my benefactor was.

Joe was the saddest to see me go. As the coach arrived to take me to London, he said in a rather quavering voice, "I still and always will remember that little Pip who would put his head through the window and watch me work in the forge. And today, I see you, on your way to London."

I had been so looking forward to my trip that I had forgotten all about Joe. Now, when it was time to bid him goodbye, I broke down completely.

Finally, I was off to London. It took me nearly five hours to reach there. The big city seemed to unnerve me. It seemed very intimidating for a young man from Kent. I immediately drove off to Mr. Jaggers' office.

Jaggers then told me what my allowance was going to be, a sum that I could not even imagine, back in the marshes. He also provided me with a list of traders, from whom I could buy on credit and the bills would be sent to Jaggers directly. This would allow him to keep a check on my expenses. After all, he was my guardian in the big city.

He introduced me to his assistant, a pleasant man called Mr. Wemmick. Considering that I had made a rough journey to London, Wemmick arranged for me to go home and take some rest, immediately. We drove to a place called Barnard's Inn. We entered one of the buildings there and went straight to the top floor. There was a note on the wall which said, 'Be right back. Door's open, make yourself comfortable.'

I stepped into a sparsely furnished, but elegant room. It was bigger than I had expected it to be. These were the quarters that I was going to share with Mr. Herbert Pocket. The Pockets were actually relatives of Miss Havisham, making me all the more confident that my benefactor was none other than Miss Havisham herself.

Wemmick left me to freshen-up. He said that he was in charge of Mr. Jaggers' cash box and therefore, we would surely be meeting each other rather frequently.

A few minutes later, Herbert Pocket came in. Right from our first meeting, I liked him a lot. He was a thorough gentleman and his manners were impeccable. Mr. Jaggers had informed me that not only would he be staying with me, but he would also be teaching me the etiquette I needed to learn.

"I realised that you would perhaps like some strawberries to go with your dinner. So I rushed off to get some," he informed me, showing me that he was truly a large-hearted person. He then

began running through the various details about the house. He mentioned that the food came from the coffee-house below. While I started to unpack, a scrumptious meal of roast chicken, bread, butter and cheese came along.

Herbert told me about himself, while we ate our dinner. He worked in a small bank, which I realised was the cause behind the little furniture that he had. He said that because of his low income, Mr. Jaggers had asked him to stay with Pip here, to teach him the smaller things that he needed to know. The manner in which he said this, made me open up to him even more. I told him the whole story behind my sudden rise to great wealth. Since I must have spoken in greater detail about Miss Havisham, Herbert decided to tell me about my own benefactor's life.

He said that Miss Havisham's mother had died when she was very young. It was her father who spoilt her. By the time he died, he left an enormous fortune. It was also about that time that she fell in love with a man, who flattered her with false declarations of love.

"My father did not like this man one bit, but Miss Havisham had been so spoilt by her father that she seldom listened to anyone else," continued Herbert. "She lent him large sums of money before the wedding. But sadly when the wedding day arrived, he simply sent her a note saying that he would not be able to marry her. This message, Pip, came in exactly at ..."

"Twenty minutes to nine," I interjected, finally solving the mystery of the stopped clocks revealing the same time. "Yes, by Jove, you are bang on! She actually stopped everything around the house at that time, and everything has been lying in the same state ever since. That is why the bridal cake has not been taken away, or why she wears that bridal gown still ... Nothing has changed in that house since that day at twenty minutes to nine," recounted Herbert.

I must also mention that during our whole conversation, Herbert did keep pointing out

several things that I was to pay attention to and learn. For instance, he told me that it was the fork and not the knife that went into the mouth, and also that the wine glass need not be raised to touch the nose while drinking it. The kindly way in which Herbert pointed out these aspects made it sound friendly and not demeaning at all.

That night, as I went to sleep for the first time in London, all that I could think of was poor Miss Havisham. I felt very sad for the lady, who had helped me realise my dreams.

9. Life in London

Soon Herbert took me to meet his father, the elder Mr. Pocket. He was as amiable as Herbert was, and we became quite close almost immediately. Besides myself, Mr. Pocket would teach two more gentlemen of my age. One of them was a man called Startop, who was a lot like Herbert and we liked each other right away. The other was a man called Bentley Drummel.

Now Drummel was a person that no one liked, and I doubted if anyone could ever like him. He was supposed to be part of some aristocracy and therefore, he would always strut around as if he were better than the rest. Herbert had told me that they called Drummel a 'spider' behind his back. Naturally, I did not take a liking to him, nor he to me.

Mr. Pocket had started to tutor me on how to become a gentleman. We would go on long walks through the streets of London, stopping by to see important monuments. I began to enjoy my new life.

At home, though, I was not very satisfied with our accommodation. It obviously lacked enough furniture. Herbert was away and so decided what to do to make it more comfortable. The next day, I met Mr. Jaggers to ask him for some money to buy some things for the house. He was eating his lunch when I met him. He heard me out, obviously thinking to himself that it did not take long for a simple boy from the countryside to learn how to live lavishly in London. He asked me how much money I needed and asked Mr. Wemmick to give me the sum.

Herbert was absolutely delighted to see the changes that I had made while he was away. I had bought the best items that I could find. My lavish new life was, however, going to have a spot of bother from my past. Biddy had written

to me that Joe was going to visit me in London in a couple of days. I was very disturbed when I read the letter. I did not want to see Joe.

On Sunday, awfully agitated at the prospect of seeing Joe again, I was shuffling around the room when I heard him walk up the steps. He had worn his best suit and had clearly bought a new hat for the visit. At first, he kept scrubbing his shoes on the mat, irritating me to no end. Then, when I was about to pull him into the room, he grabbed my hands and started shaking them like a pump. I was greatly embarrassed at all this.

However, my luck changed soon enough as Herbert came in along with a waiter who brought our lunch. I tried to take Joe's hat, but he would not give it to me, as if it were made of gold. At lunch, Joe succeeded in embarrassing me further. First he kept his hat on top of the fireplace, from where it kept falling. As it fell every time, Joe would reach out from his chair and put it back exactly at the same spot. He sat so far away from the table that half his food never reached his mouth! I did not know what to do.

Luckily, Herbert left us for a while after lunch to attend to something. Now that we were alone, Joe turned to me and said, "I must say I enjoyed that meal, Sir ..."

I shook off his hand and screamed at him. "Sir? How can you call me that, Joe?"

"I shouldn't have come here, Pip. I don't belong here. I should have remained in my forge. If you ever want to come and meet me, you know where to find me," so saying, and without another word, Joe was gone. I could only breathe a sigh of relief.

Some sad news came in towards the end of the week. Biddy wrote to say that my sister had died.

But then, came the best news of all – Estella was in London and she wanted me to call on her. This was the happiest day of my life!

10. Estella

I was over the moon when I read Estella's letter. Herbert obviously must have read the excitement on my face. He kept smiling at me for a long time. Unable to conceal my happiness, I told him about my feelings for Estella and how I was in love with her.

To this, came Herbert's prompt reply, "Oh, I already know about that." I looked at him surprised. How could he know about it because I had surely not told him anything? "You see, I knew it from the time you told me about your visits to Miss Havisham in your childhood. It was written all over your face!"

Overjoyed that my friend already knew about my feelings, I went on to tell him about how the old Miss Havisham must have wanted that I marry Estella. Why else would she go through all the trouble to make me a gentleman otherwise? Now Herbert's face turned sombre.

"Pip, may I please tell you something?" he asked. Still reeling under the excitement of being able to see Estella shortly, I asked him to go on. "Well, I just wanted to tell you that in case it is not mentioned by your benefactor to marry Estella, I would ask you not to think about her too much."

I was shocked to hear Herbert say these words. However, I just motioned him to go on. He continued, "You see, Pip, before I go any further, let me tell you that I have someone in my life. Her name is Clara and I would like you to meet her sometime soon."

This thing had obviously never crossed my mind when Herbert had begun, but anyway, I did not bother about it now. Herbert went on to say, "Now think about the way in which Estella has been brought up. Miss Havisham has brought her up to be cold and heartless, to break the hearts

of men, just like the man who broke her heart. Stay away, my dear Pip, because Estella will only break your heart."

After he finished, I could only reply, "I thank you for your concern, Herbert, I really do. But there is no way in which I can detach myself from her. I am madly in love with her, like I have been from the first day that I saw her. I am sorry but I cannot do as you say."

Soon it was time for my twenty-first birthday. To mark the occasion, Mr. Jaggers allowed me to handle my money on my own from now on. He did obviously keep tabs on how well I did with the fat five hundred pounds a year allowance. However, from then on, I did what I wanted to do, without anyone lording over me. It was truly a wonderful feeling!

The minute Jaggers handed me the money, I decided to do one thing before spending the money on anything else. I went to meet a small-time shipping merchant, called Clarriker. With him I worked out an arrangement, wherein, I would keep paying him a certain sum of money over time and he would in turn make Herbert a partner in his company. You can understand my happiness when in the evening, Herbert told me that he bumped into a certain person named, Clarriker and found a new, high-paying job. Herbert, for one, did not have to know who his benefactor was. The look on his face was enough for me.

Meanwhile, Estella's fame had grown in London. She was called for all the parties that took place in the city, and she would ask me to escort her to each and every one of them. While I should have been overjoyed at this proposal, my problem was that she always treated me as a kind of half-brother, or perhaps I could have passed off as her employee. She even told me once, "Will you never learn?" As it was, I was annoyed for quite some time now with her behaviour and replied, "Learn about you and the way you treat me?" She never did reply and walked off, claiming that I was blind.

One day, Estella called on me and asked to be escorted to visit Miss Havisham. I realised that

though she could have perhaps made this journey on her own, she needed my company during the long drive home and I readily agreed to go with her.

Miss Havisham was delighted to see Estella again. She kept staring at her and stroking her hand, overjoyed, I imagine, at seeing the beautiful revenge she had planned on men. During the conversation, I realised that she went on clawing Estella, and at one point, Estella pulled herself back.

"You are stone-hearted! Do you hate me?" asked a perturbed Miss Havisham.

Estella replied in her usual and cold way, "You made me this way. Why are you bothered?"

"But I always taught you to love me ... Break their hearts, not mine. Is that not what I have taught you?" demanded Miss Havisham.

The fight started to get pretty heated up and I decided that it would be best if I left the room. Even though I had climbed down the steps and was almost about to reach the door, I could still hear Miss Havisham's voice crackling loudly.

11. Finally, We Meet!

I realised that handling my money was not very easy. I was now twenty-three years old and heavily in debt! I also came to realise that the sum that seemed enormous to me at twenty-one was actually rather small. At least I still remembered the time when I was twenty-one! I had never given a passing glance to the young boy in the marshes.

I did not have to go to Mr. Pocket anymore, but would rather stay at home and mostly read. It was on one such day when I was reading at home that it happened. It had been raining pretty heavily throughout the day and therefore, I did not feel like going out. Herbert, too, had gone out of the country on some work for Clarriker. The bell tower outside had just chimed eleven times.

I was just about to go to bed, when suddenly there was a knock on the door.

I took my light with me and opened it. A rather old, sunburnt man was standing there. He kept looking at me for quite some time, but I could not recognise him. After a while, I asked him, "Yes, how may I help you?"

The man did not answer right away. He kept looking at me for a while longer and then said, "I came here to look for Mr. Pip."

"I am Pip," I replied. "What can I do for you?" He did not say anything, but kept peeking inside over my shoulder. I understood that he wanted to come in and so I stepped away and gestured him to come in.

At first he looked around. Then he gave an appreciative glance. I could not make out what was going on through this man's mind. I wondered if he was mad. He glanced at the bottles in the small bar in the corner of the room and asked, "May I have a drink?"

I stood up flabbergasted, not knowing how to respond to that question. I thought that if I would

humour him, he would perhaps go away. So I poured him a small glass. All this while, he was looking around the house. He even made himself comfortable on my easy chair.

Now, with a drink in his hand, sitting in my chair, he gave me a hard stare. His lips were twisted in a crooked smile. "You still don't recognise me, do you?" he asked again.

I just stood there, transfixed. I tried hard but could not remember him. Suddenly, before I could even move, he jumped on me and yelled into my ear, "Stop that or I'll tear you to pieces." It came rushing back to me. I knew who the man was. He was my convict, from the marshes of Kent!

He understood the look of recognition on my face and broke out laughing. Then he stopped and said, "I'm sorry about that. I just came to say thank you for all that you had done for me that night. I have never forgotten that night. You came to me like my guardian angel."

He tried to embrace me, but I was too scared to even acknowledge. I pushed him away and said, "Well, you needn't have come all this way to thank me. But thank you anyway. You may leave now."

He once again sat down on the easy chair and said, "Let me finish my drink at least!" I naturally had to agree to that, and tried to start a conversation to while away the time. I asked him what had happened to him since the time I had seen him last. "Oh, I was let off, but I had to leave the country. I went to New South Wales and became a farmer and did pretty well in my life. But what about you, Pip? How do you manage to live on five hundred pounds a year?"

I almost spilt my drink on hearing this! How did this man know the exact amount of my allowance? I stared at him as he continued. "And tell Jaggers that I am very happy with what he has done so far. Wemmick too. Nice chaps, all of them."

Only then did my whole world come crashing down around me. I finally understood what was happening. The convict that I had met in the marshes of Kent that wet Christmas morning,

the man who was now in front of me, was my secret benefactor!

It seemed that he had been able to read my mind and confirmed, "That's right! It's me ... It has been me all along!"

Saying this, he finished his drink in one long gulp and got up to leave. I was still in a state of shock and I did not know what was happening around me, or what I should do. Just as he reached the door, he turned to me once again and said, "I just had to come, to see you once, and I have. There is nothing else left for me. Thank you so much once again, Pip."

He opened the door and was just about step out, when I said, "It's pretty late now. You can stay here for the night and leave tomorrow morning."

He seemed to appreciate that and came back in, closing the door behind him. "That would be nice. After all, it would be dangerous for me to go out now."

"Dangerous?" I said. "I don't understand what you mean?"

"Oh, you see," he explained, "When I was let off, I was told that I was never to return to England ever again. Else they said I'd be hanged!" It did not seem that he cared much about the penalty.

He sat down on the chair once again and said, "But don't you worry, they won't be able to recognise me. Look what I have got here ... Spectacles, plus I've dyed my hair and who would think there could be a convict under these rich clothes. You've got nothing to worry about, my boy!"

He seemed rather happy to be with me. He went on with his story, "You see my boy, you mean more to me than a real son would. As soon as I started making money as a farmer in New South Wales, I decided that every pound that I ever earned should go to you. I starved so that you could get the money, my son. And today that I see you, I am so proud of you."

I let him sleep in Herbert's room that night. I did not sleep at all. I was made into a gentleman with a convict's money! It was not Miss Havisham

after all. She had made no plans for me. Estella, Miss Havisham, Joe, Jaggers, Wemmick, Herbert, everyone just kept rushing through my head as I stared into the fireplace.

12. Now What?

My convict's name was Abel Magwitch. I knew that I could not let him wander into the city, even if it were just to see him leave the country forever. First, I decided to let my landlady know that my uncle had come to visit me. I knew that I could let Magwitch use Herbert's room temporarily. What would I do after Herbert's return?

After breakfast, Magwitch seated himself and lit his pipe with some foul-smelling tobacco. I decided to have a talk with him. "For how long will you be in the country?" I asked. "Oh, I am not going back. I have decided to die here," came the reply.

Now it was my turn to be shocked. He once again pointed out his rich clothes as a disguise, but I suggested a farmer's outfit according to his skin tone. He agreed and I went off to buy him his new clothes. First, I had to go somewhere else.

As I entered Jaggers' office, I saw both Jaggers and Wemmick exchange looks with each other and then the statutory warning flashed before me, 'No names'.

I looked at Jaggers and said, "A gentleman came into my house yesterday. He says he is my benefactor. Is that true?"

Jaggers nodded in agreement.

"I thought it was Miss Havisham," I replied, hoping he would change his answer.

"I never led you on to believe that; this was planted in your head by Miss Havisham herself," he replied in his usual business-like tone.

Now I was completely convinced that Magwitch was indeed my benefactor. I returned to find Herbert sitting and talking to Magwitch. I looked at Magwitch and his look told me that he had not told Herbert anything yet.

After another five minutes, Magwitch gave me a look, which told me that he trusted Herbert, and

I could tell him everything, if I wanted to. Herbert was interested in the whole story and promised never to tell anyone about Magwitch. Now we had another problem on our hands. We had to find another place for Magwitch.

Herbert suggested a place by the river, close to where his fiancée, Clara, lived. He said it would be the ideal place for Magwitch to hide and no one would ever get to know that he had been a convict at one time. Even Magwitch considered this a viable option.

Later, Herbert sought me out and told me, "The house by the river will do fine for now, Pip. But we will have to get him out of the country. It is for his own sake that I am saying this."

I replied, "I agree with you. But the problem is that he will not leave without me."

"Then you have to go with him," came Herbert's obvious solution. I knew that Herbert was speaking the truth. If, for Magwitch's safety I had to leave with him, then so be it. Maybe I could return after he was out of the country, but there was no reason to let Magwitch know about that yet.

We soon took Magwitch to the house Herbert had suggested and settled him down. I also met Clara, while we were there. She was a fine woman and I was very happy for Herbert. I congratulated my friend at his fortunate match.

Herbert had to go to Clarriker's office, so I decided to go home and think about what to do next. As I entered the house, I saw a man waiting for me. Wemmick! Before I could even open my mouth, Wemmick motioned me to keep silent. Intrigued at his action, I tiptoed across to where he was sitting and sat down on the chair next to him.

In a hushed tone he began saying, "Mr. Pip, I have come to talk about your new guest. This is a rather serious matter and therefore, I would like you to keep this strictly between ourselves and least of all tell your 'uncle' about it." I nodded in agreement and he continued, "You see, there is a man in the city called Compeyson, who has been spreading the news that a man from New South Wales has come to London. Very soon the

authorities will also get wind of the fact and then there will be trouble for your 'uncle'. We have to work fast in getting him out of this country."

I could feel a cold chill crawl through my spine as I heard this. I immediately put Wemmick in the picture and told him about our plans to leave the city. He suggested that we leave the city by the Hamburg Steamer and go away to Germany. He declared that we would be safe there.

When Herbert returned, I told him everything that had transpired between Wemmick and myself. Herbert immediately suggested that we hire a boat and begin the whole exercise. However, once our plans were finalised, Herbert turned to me and said, "What was the name of the man that Wemmick gave you? Compeyson?"

I nodded, not understanding why Herbert was so perturbed by Compeyson and when he told me, I must admit, it took me by surprise as well. "Pip, Compeyson was Miss Havisham's beloved. He is the man who did not turn up on their wedding day. The very same Compeyson!"

13. Fire!

My own monetary condition was rather poor at that time. I started to sell my rings, my watches, anything that I could lay my hands on to get some money. Moreover, I also had to pay the last instalment to Clarriker for Herbert. I decided that for the latter, I would approach Miss Havisham and take a small loan from her.

I went to meet Jaggers and told him about the whole plan. As we were talking, Jaggers' old maid came over with his lunch. She seemed to trip over my outstretched leg and turned to look at me, apparently with disgust. Only then did I get a good look at her face. Why, it seemed so familiar! And then I remembered whom she looked like. Estella! She looked exactly like Estella! After she left, giving me a nasty glare,

I asked Jaggers about who she was, but all he told me was that she had murdered another woman in a jealous fit. Jaggers had been able to successfully defend her. She remained in my mind for a long time afterwards.

As I rode off to Miss Havisham's after I finished with Jaggers, his maid's story kept flashing through my head. She had killed another woman in a jealous fit over her husband, and supposedly, she even killed her little infant daughter. The daughter had to be Estella! The resemblance was too uncanny.

As I reached Miss Havisham's, I found that she had grown older and weaker. I told her about my deal with Clarriker and how I needed the money to make the last payment for Herbert. Miss Havisham heard me out and replied, "His father had once given me some advice, which I did not take. I have paid the price for that during my whole life. I will give you the money, but please make sure that he does not get to know about it."

I nodded in agreement and she immediately gave me a note to give to Jaggers, instructing him to give me the money from her account.

As I took the note, Miss Havisham kept staring at the fire and said, "She has left me as well. Do you see what she has made me?"

I tried to feel sorry for the old lady, but compassion was not something that she deserved. After all, she had made Estella this way. I also had to tell her something. So I walked up to her, took her hand in mine and placed it on my chest. I said, "Do you know what this is? It's my heart and it is broken!"

She wailed and said, "Oh what have I done? What have I done? Pip, will you please forgive me? This is not what I wanted. Oh, please forgive me, Pip!"

"I forgive you!" is all that I could bring myself to say.

No sooner had I finished, I raced down the steps, angry and humiliated. Before I could leave the house, a shriek from Miss Havisham made

me swing around. There she was at the top of the steps, her whole veil on fire. I immediately ran up to her and tried to smother the flames. My own hands got burnt pretty badly, but I was able to save Miss Havisham.

14. The Escape

In London, the next day we took a small boat; one convenient enough to smuggle Magwitch out in. There was only one problem now. My hands were in bandages after the incident at Miss Havisham's house. While my injury was not the reason for concern, we were now one man short to row the boat. Herbert at once suggested that we contact Startop, the young man who studied with me at Mr. Pocket's. I agreed, because he was a very nice fellow and we would be able to trust him.

While we were planning Magwitch's escape, Estella summoned me one evening. When I reached her house, she informed me that she was marrying Bentley Drummel. I was shocked to hear about her choice. I tried to reason with her, but her answer was prompt. She said, "Don't think that I will keep him happy!" This was no reason to get married to someone, I explained. But how could I, a common peasant boy, convince Estella? I came back disappointed.

We reached Magwitch's house in the evening. He was first very concerned to see my hands in bandages. Then we told him about the whole plan of escape. We were going to pick him up early next morning. We would then row to the bay, where we would be in time for the Hamburg Steamer. I was to go with him. This news brought great relief to Magwitch.

The next morning, things went as planned. We picked up Magwitch and started to move towards the bay. We reached our destination well within time to see the Hamburg Steamer approach us. Suddenly, another boat came over in our direction. It seemed to be a police boat. A man, covered in a cloak, seemed to be leading the police over to us. Suddenly a man yelled at us, "We know that a convict is in that boat. Help us in capturing him!"

As soon as the boat came right alongside us, Magwitch leapt up and pulled the man's cloak away from him. It was the second man that I had seen in the marshes that night! He tried to pull away from Magwitch, but it was too late. Even at this age, Magwitch sprang up and knocked him over. Our own boat capsized. The Hamburg Steamer was right above us. Other boats too got into the fray, and saved us from drowning. When they found Magwitch, he was bleeding from a deep cut on his head. The other man, Compeyson, could not be found, till they dragged his body out much later.

We had been caught. Magwitch, alas, could not escape.

15. Abel Magwitch

The police took Magwitch into custody immediately. They took him to a hospital, as his wound looked very grave. I had to hand over everything that belonged to him, but the police allowed me to stay with him at the hospital.

Magwitch regained consciousness after a few days. He grasped my hand and said, "Don't feel sorry about the whole thing, m'boy! I don't have any regrets. Though, I think I should tell you my entire story before I die."

Then, clinging to me, Magwitch recounted his story.

"'I used to work for a gentleman. Well, we did all kinds of nasty work, but we had our work cut out. This gentleman, Compeyson, would plan the whole thing and I would carry it out. So in the event that we were caught, he would go free and I would be the one who would have to pay the price for it.

"We did manage to carry on rather well, but one day, we were caught by the police. I was sure that Compeyson, who needed me to do his dirty work, would get me out easily enough. But the first thing that he asked for was a separate hearing for the two of us. There he started to give the court, evidence against me.

"Now who would you believe? A common peasant, or a gentleman in rich clothes? Needless to say, the court believed every word of his, and did not even give me a second glance. I was sent off to prison, while he went off to cheat some rich woman in Kent. I later learnt that he had been caught by the police and had been sent to prison.

"I decided to hunt him down, even if it was the last thing I ever did. That is why you saw me fighting with him in the marshes that night. I could have escaped, but there was no way I would let him escape.

"That, my son, is my story. The rest of it you already know."

Then Magwitch let go of my hand and sank back into his bed. I wanted to know more about the man who had given me such a lavish future. I asked him, "And don't you have any family?"

"Aye, I did once," he replied. "I had a wife and a little girl."

"But you never told me about them. Where are they now?" I asked.

He turned to me feebly and said, "You see, my wife, she was not right in the head. She always had this fear that I took fancy to some other woman and one day, in a fit of anger she went and killed this woman. All this was just a figment of her imagination. When I tried to calm her down, she threatened that she would kill my infant girl as well."

He continued, "But then the authorities caught up with her and they took her away. I had to go into hiding, for then I would have to give evidence against my own wife. It was there that

I heard about Mr. Jaggers and how he had been able to successfully save my wife. I never got to know what became of my girl ... I just think that my wife must have killed her in a fit."

I understood what he was talking about. I knew the woman, Magwitch's wife! It was Jaggers' maid. The stories matched. And that meant Estella was none other than Magwitch's daughter. Magwitch had gone back to sleep and so I did not disturb him any further.

16. Death

Magwitch was still very weak when his trial began. Jaggers did his best to convince the jury that his client was now a changed man in New South Wales and he should be given another chance. The jury would offer him no mercy and charged him. He was to die within a few days.

I prayed that Magwitch would die even before the date of his execution. I went to see him at the prison hospital every day. His health was deteriorating. There were times when he did not even know that I was in the room.

One day, as I entered, I heard his voice call out to me. "My dear boy, you are always the first one to see me."

I replied, "I stand by the gate and the minute they open up, I come rushing in."

He smiled weakly and replied, "Ah, my dear boy, you stood by me through my darkest hours. And you seem more close to me now than you did, when we first met."

He then went into a coughing bout. After he stopped, he seemed to have lost all his energy. I crept real close to him and said in his ear, "Magwitch, old friend, there is something that I need to tell you."

He just pressed my hand a little stronger to tell me that he could hear me. "Your daughter, she is alive. She lives with powerful friends now and she is a very intelligent and pretty lady. And I must confess that I am in love with her."

At these words, Magwitch only held my hand harder. He then went into another coughing fit. I tried to break away from him, but he would not let me go. He pulled me closer and whispered, "Thank you, my son, thank you!"

Those were his last words. Magwitch breathed his last that day!

17. A New Life

After Magwitch's death, everything changed in my life again. I had to give away my house in order to pay off some bills. I also went to Clarriker and paid him the last installment for Herbert. Now, he was a partner at the firm. Herbert later informed me that he would have to go to Egypt to set up the new offices of Clarriker. Before leaving, he informed me that a position would always be open for me at Clarriker's. I could not thank him enough for all that he had done for me during my troubled times with Magwitch.

The strain of clearing my debts caught up with me soon. I fell into a state of heavy delirium and fever. I would keep screaming in my sleep and there was no one there to help me.

One day, when I opened my eyes, I found someone sitting next to me. He was administering a cold compress on my forehead. As he saw me open my eyes, he said, "Take it easy now, Pip! You need to take rest."

I realised that though I had deserted this man, he had not left me. When there was no one left for me, Joe had come from Kent to take care of me. He stayed with me all through my sickness, nursing me, looking after me. When he felt that I was better, he left, as silently as he had come. When I was able to walk around, I saw all my pending bills lying on the table; each one of them had been paid.

I decided that I belonged in Kent and so I should return there. I even thought about asking Biddy to marry me. We had been very close in our youth and she would be the ideal girl for me.

When I did reach my house in Kent again, I saw a small crowd gathered all around. New curtains were fluttering in the wind and there was an air of celebration all around. As I approached, I saw

the reason for the festivities. Joe and Biddy had married. I soon forgot everything and rejoiced in their happiness.

Joe was ecstatic at seeing me and Biddy gave me a huge, warm hug. I decided to stay on there for some more time, being with the people who were always there for me when I needed them the most.

I learnt from Joe, later, that Miss Havisham had finally succumbed to her wounds. She had left everything she owned to Estella. Then I told Joe about my benefactor, right from the first time that I had met him in the marshes. He listened to my story with wide-eyed awe.

After spending some time in Kent, I went back to London and sold off everything that I ever had and settled all my remaining debts. Herbert had got married to Clara and asked me to move in with him. I also took up the post of a clerk in Clarriker's and was eventually made a partner. We may not have been the biggest firm in the country, but we were one of the most respectable ones.

Clarriker, one day, confessed to Herbert about how I had got him his partnership in the firm. After which, Herbert never ceased to thank me for it.

I now lived on my own, safe and secure. My great expectations had not worked out, but I was at least happy with my life now.

18. There She Was

It had been almost ten years since I went back to Kent. I had been writing to Joe and Biddy regularly. I was in for a surprise when I walked into the forge and put my head in through the window, for old times' sake. Joe was sitting by the furnace, reading, while a small boy of about four sat there in front of him.

Joe rushed to hug me, calling out for Biddy. She came out to greet me. And I was then introduced to little Pip. Yes, they had named their son Pip, after me. Little Pip and I got along very well. I took him to see the graves of my parents.

I decided to go back one last time to Miss Havisham's. I saw that the old house had deteriorated further. A portion of it had fallen off and the hall could be seen from outside now. I stood under a tree and kept staring at the house for a long time. A large portion of my life was spent here, resulting in hope, expectations and speculations.

It was getting dark and I was just about to leave, when suddenly someone called out my name. I turned around to see Estella standing there behind me.

"What are you doing here?" I asked.

She motioned towards the house and said, "This was the last thing that I had, and I have just sold it off. I just came to look at it one last time."

She then mentioned how her marriage to Bentley Drummel had been the most horrible marriage one could think of. She had left him almost two years ago and had heard that he had, subsequently, died in a riding accident.

"I am a changed person now, Pip. I have learnt it the hard way. I realise now what a fool I have been. And to think I spurned you. You were the

only person who ever loved me. And I treated you so badly," she said, as she started to cry.

I held her close to me and said, "Estella, we have both learnt our lessons and we are both changed people now. It is time that we move on and perhaps, start all over again."

"There have been times that I have thought of you, Pip, and then tried to forget about you, remembering the way I always treated you. But I just want you to know that you always had a special place in my heart," she declared.

"And you always will have a special place in my heart, Estella," I concluded. "We were friends and we shall always remain friends."

Thus, hand in hand, we walked away from there, leaving the shadows of Miss Havisham and of the past behind us forever.

About the Author

■ Charles Dickens

Charles Dickens was born on February 7, 1812, to John and Elizabeth Dickens. His father, a clerk in the Naval Pay Office, was imprisoned for debt. Charles, then, was put to work at Warren's Blacking Factory until his father was released and finally rescued him. Between 1824 and 1827, Dickens read at a school in London and when he turned fifteen, he was employed as an office boy at an attorney's office.

It is well-known that his turbulent times were the source of his creative inspiration – and they emerge most strongly in his works *David Copperfield* and *Great Expectations.*

Great Expectations (1861) is Charles Dickens's thirteenth novel. It is the second novel, after *David Copperfield,* to be fully narrated in the first person. *Great Expectations* is a bildungsroman, or a coming-of-age novel, and the story genre is Victorian Literature

After the success of his *Pickwick Papers,* Dickens chose to a full-time novelist, though still contributing through his journalistic and editorial services.

In 1859, Dickens began a new weekly in London, called *All the Year Round.* He continued to write great gems in English Literature that are read and praised till date and always will be. Till his very end, Dickens held the editorial responsibility of *All the Year Round,* held readings and wrote his novels.

His final reading was in London in 1870, and he suffered a massive stroke on June 8 and passed away on June 9. He was buried at Westminister Abbey on June 14, 1870.

■ Characters

Pip: The protagonist and narrator of the novel, Pip began the story as a young orphan boy being raised by his sister and brother-in-law in the marsh country of Kent, in the southeast of England. Pip was passionate, romantic, and somewhat unrealistic at heart, and he tended to expect more for himself than is reasonable. Pip also had a powerful conscience, and he deeply wanted to improve himself, both morally and socially.

Estella: Miss Havisham's beautiful young ward, Estella was Pip's unattainable dream throughout the novel. He loved her passionately, but, though she sometimes seems to consider him a friend, she was usually cold, cruel, and uninterested in him. As they grew up together, she repeatedly warned him that she has no heart.

Miss Havisham: Miss Havisham was the wealthy, eccentric old woman who lived in a manor called Satis House near Pip's village. She was a manic and often seemed insane, flitting around her house in a faded wedding dress, keeping a decaying feast on her table, and surrounding herself with clocks stopped at twenty minutes to nine. As a young woman, Miss Havisham was jilted by her fiancé minutes before her wedding, and now she has a vendetta against all men. She deliberately raised Estella to be the tool of her revenge, training her beautiful ward to break men's hearts.

Abel Magwitch ("The Convict"): A fearsome criminal, Magwitch escaped from prison at the beginning of the novel and terrorized Pip in the cemetery. Pip's kindness, however, made a deep impression on him, and he subsequently devoted himself to making a fortune and using it to elevate Pip into a higher social class. Behind the scenes, he becomes Pip's secret benefactor, funding Pip's education and opulent lifestyle in London through the lawyer Jaggers.

Joe Gargery: Pip's brother-in-law, the village blacksmith, Joe stayed with his overbearing, abusive wife—known as Mrs. Joe—solely out of love for Pip. Although he is uneducated and unrefined, he consistently acted for the benefit of those he loved and suffered in silence when Pip treated him coldly.

Jaggers: The powerful, foreboding lawyer hired by Magwitch to supervise Pip's elevation to the upper class. As one of the most important criminal lawyers in London, Jaggers was privy to some dirty business; he consorted with vicious criminals, and even they were terrified of him. He often seemed to care for Pip, and before the novel began he helps Miss Havisham to adopt the orphaned Estella.

Herbert Pocket: Pip first met Herbert Pocket in the garden of Satis House, when, as a pale young gentleman, Herbert challenged him to a fight. Years later, they meet again in London, and Herbert becomes Pip's best friend and key companion after Pip's elevation to the status of gentleman. He hoped to become a merchant so that he can afford to marry Clara Barley.

Wemmick: Jaggers's clerk and Pip's friend. At work, he was hard, cynical, sarcastic, and obsessed with "portable property"; at home in Walworth, he was jovial, wry, and a tender caretaker of his "Aged Parent."

Biddy: A simple, kindhearted country girl, Biddy first befriended Pip when they attend school together. After Mrs. Joe was attacked and became an invalid, Biddy moved into Pip's home to care for her. Throughout most of the novel, Biddy represented the opposite of Estella; she was plain, kind, moral, and of Pip's own social class.

Mrs. Joe: Pip's sister and Joe's wife, known only as "Mrs. Joe" throughout the novel. Mrs. Joe was a stern and overbearing figure to both Pip and Joe. She kept a spotless household and frequently menaced her husband and her brother with her cane. She later met with an accident and later passed away.

Uncle Pumblechook: Pip's pompous, arrogant uncle. A merchant obsessed with money, Pumblechook was responsible for arranging Pip's first meeting with Miss Havisham. Throughout the rest of the novel, he shamelessly took credit for Pip's rise in social status, even though he had nothing to do with it, since Magwitch, not Miss Havisham, is Pip's secret benefactor

Compeyson: A criminal and the former partner of Magwitch, Compeyson is an educated, gentlemanly outlaw who contrasted sharply with the coarse and uneducated Magwitch. Compeyson was responsible for Magwitch's capture at the end of the novel. He was also the man who jilted Miss Havisham on her wedding day.

Molly: Jaggers's housekeeper. Later, Pip realises that she was Estella's mother.

Startop: A friend of Pip's and Herbert's. Startop was a delicate young man who, with Pip and Drummle, took tutelage with Matthew Pocket. Later, Startop helped Pip and Herbert with Magwitch's escape.

Miss Skiffins: Wemmick's beloved, and eventual wife.

■ Questions

Chapter 1
- Who did Pip meet at the graveyard? On what condition did he let Pip go?
- Why did the convict ask Pip to get a file?

Chapter 2
- Why was Pip confused when he went to meet the convict?

Chapter 3
- Why did Pip get scared to see the policemen dangling a pair of handcuffs in front of him?
- What did the convict confess while being taken away by the policemen?

Chapter 4
- What kind of offer did Uncle Pumblechook have for Pip?
- Describe Pip's impression of Miss Havisham.
- Why was Estella rude to Pip?
- What realisation was made by Pip by the end of his first meeting with Miss Havisham and Estella?

Chapter 5
- Why did Miss Havisham tell Pip not to ever come back to meet them?

Chapter 6
- Why did Pip take a day off from work? Where did he go?
- Why did Pip decide to become a gentleman?

Chapter 7
- What offer did Mr. Jagger make for Pip's future to Joe?
- Who did Pip think was his benefactor?

Chapter 8
- Who was appointed to teach Pip etiquette?
- What did Herbert tell Pip about Miss Havisham?

Chapter 9
- *Why was Pip so uncomfortable during Joe's visit? How did Joe take the insult?*

Chapter 10
- *What warning did Herbert give Pip about Estella?*
- *Why was Miss Havisham sad about Estella?*

Chapter 11
- *Who turns out to be Pip's benefactor? How did Pip react to it?*

Chapter 12
- *What was Pip's benefactor's name?*
- *Who was Compeyson and what connection does he have with Miss Havisham?*

Chapter 13
- *What did Pip tell Miss Havisham, which made her apologise to him?*

Chapter 14
- *Who did Estella decide to marry?*
- *How was Magwitch finally caught by the police?*

Chapter 15
- *What was the connection between Magwitch, Molly and Estella?*

Chapter 16
- *What did Pip tell Magwitch before his death?*

Chapter 17
- *Who got married to Biddy? What was her son's name?*

Chapter 18
- *Who did Pip reunite with in the end?*